The clearest way into the universe is through a forest wilderness.

JOHN MUIR
(1838–1914)
Scottish-born American naturalist

Canadian representatives: General Publishing Co., Ltd.,
30 Lesmill Road, Don Mills, Ontario M3B 2T6.
International representatives: Worldwide Media Services, Inc.,
30 Montgomery Street, Jersey City, New Jersey 07302.

ISBN 1–56138–070–9

Cover design by Toby Schmidt
Interior design by Nancy Loggins
Cover: Albrecht Dürer, *The Large Piece of Turf*, Vienna, Kunsthistorische Museum.
Nimatallah/Art Resource, New York
Interior illustrations by Kathryn Borosky
Typography: CG Palacio by Richard Conklin

This book may be ordered by mail from the publisher.
Please add $2.50 for postage and handling.
But try your bookstore first!
Running Press Book Publishers
125 South Twenty-second Street
Philadelphia, Pennsylvania 19103

NATURE

RUNNING PRESS
Philadelphia, Pennsylvania

Put your ear close to the whispering branch and you may catch what it is saying.

GUY MURCHIE
20th-century American educator and writer

E*arth laughs in flowers.*

RALPH WALDO EMERSON
(1803–1882)
American essayist and poet

I have walked this south stream when to believe in spring was an act of faith. It was spitting snow and blowing, and within two days of being May. . . . But as if to assert the triumph of climate over weather, one ancient willow managed a few gray pussy willows, soft and barely visible against the snow-blurred gray background.

ANN ZWINGER
b. 1925
American writer and artist

Every moment Nature starts on the longest journey, and every moment she reaches her goal.

J.W. VON GOETHE
(1749–1832)
German poet

The natural world is dynamic. From the expanding universe to the hair on a baby's head, nothing is the same from now to the next moment.

HELEN HOOVER
b. 1910
American naturalist and writer

By spring the fallen leaves on the stream bed will all have been swept away, and the water, filtered once again through the air and ground, will take back the clear taste of the rock. I drink the cool brew of the autumn.

WENDELL BERRY
b. 1934
American writer

To enjoy scenery you should ramble amidst it; let the feelings to which it gives rise mingle with other thoughts; look round upon it in intervals of reading; and not go to it as one goes to see the lions fed at a fair. The beautiful is not to be stared at, but to be lived with.

THOMAS BABINGTON
MACAULEY
(1800–1859)
English writer and statesman

A nature lover is a person who, when treed by a bear, enjoys the view.

ANONYMOUS

Like boys on dolphins, the continents ride their crystal plates. New lands shoulder up from the waves, and old lands buckle under.

ANNIE DILLARD
b. 1945
American writer

In nature things move violently to their place, and calmly in their place.

FRANCIS BACON
(1561–1626)
English philosopher

Parting the water, the great mantas catapult into the sky, spinning white bellies to the sun—black, white, white, black. Slowly they fall into the sea. In the windlessness the falls resound from the horizons.

PETER MATTHIESSEN
b. 1927
American writer and naturalist

E*verything the Power of the World does is done in a circle. The Sky is round and I have heard that the earth is round like a ball and so are all the stars. The Wind, in its greatest power, whirls.*

BLACK ELK
(1863–1950)
Native American writer and cultural historian

There is no other door to knowledge than the door Nature opens; and there is no truth except the truths we discover in Nature.

LUTHER BURBANK
(1849–1926)
American horticulturist

Tract upon tract of arrow bamboo danced in the wind like a solid ocean reaching far to the horizon, and on this ocean red clouds drifted. No! They were alpine rhododendrons bursting with joy.

TANG XIYANG
b. 1930
Chinese naturalist and writer

N ature is pleased with simplicity, and
affects not the pomp of superfluous
causes.

ISAAC NEWTON
(1642–1727)
English scientist

It were happy if we studied nature more in natural things, and acted according to nature, whose rules are few, plain, and most reasonable.

WILLIAM PENN
(1644–1718)
Quaker founder of Pennsylvania

...to find the universal elements
enough; to find the air and the water
exhilarating; to be refreshed by a
morning walk or an evening saunter...to
be thrilled by the stars at night; to be
elated over a bird's nest or a wild flower
in spring—these are some of the rewards
of the simple life.

JOHN BURROUGHS
(1837–1921)
American naturalist and writer

The day, water, sun, moon, night—I do not have to purchase these things with money.

PLAUTUS
(254?–184 B.C.)
Roman playwright

Desert is a loose term to indicate land that supports no man; whether the land can be bitted and broken to that purpose is not proven. Void of life it never is, however dry the air and villainous the soil.

MARY AUSTIN
(1868–1934)
American writer

The coyote lives chiefly in the most desolate and forbidding deserts, along with the lizards, the jackass-rabbit and the raven, and gets an uncertain and precarious living, and earns it.

MARK TWAIN
(1835–1910)
American writer

The everlasting universe of things
Flows through the mind, and rolls its
rapid wave.

PERCY BYSSHE SHELLEY
(1792–1822)
English poet

To create a little flower is the labour of ages.

WILLIAM BLAKE
(1757–1827)
English artist and poet

Nature chose for a tool, not the earthquake or lightning to rend and split asunder, not the stormy torrent or eroding rain, but the tender snow-flowers noiselessly falling through unnumbered centuries. . . .

JOHN MUIR
(1838–1914)
Scottish-born American naturalist

Boon nature scattered, free and wild,
Each plant or flower, the mountain's
child.

SIR WALTER SCOTT
(1771–1832)
Scottish writer

. . . I have felt the inexplicable but sharply boosted intensity of a wild moment in the bush, where it is not until some minutes later that you discover the source of electricity—the warm remains of a grizzle bear kill, or the still moist tracks of a wolverine.

BARRY LOPEZ
b. 1945
American writer

Then he saw the bear. It did not emerge, appear: it was just there, immobile, fixed in the green and windless noon's hot dappling, not as big as he had dreamed it but as big as he had expected, bigger, dimensionless against the dappled obscurity, looking at him.

WILLIAM FAULKNER
(1897–1962)
American writer

After you have exhausted what there
is in business, politics, conviviality, and
so on . . .what remains? Nature remains.

WALT WHITMAN
(1819–1892)
American poet

You can't be suspicious of a tree, or accuse a bird or a squirrel of subversion or challenge the ideology of a violet.

HAL BORLAND
(1900–1978)
American writer

...the most obvious attribute of the cosmos is its impermanence. It assumes the aspect not so much of a permanent entity as of a changeful process, in which naught endures save the flow of energy and the rational order which pervades it.

THOMAS HUXLEY
(1825–1895)
English biologist

Nature is a mutable cloud which is always and never the same.

RALPH WALDO EMERSON
(1803–1882)
American essayist and poet

Rocks and clay are part of the Mother.
They emerge in various forms, but at
some time before, they were smaller
particles of great boulders. At a later time
they may again become what they once
were. Dust.

LESLIE MARMON SILKO
b. 1948
American writer

Everything that physicists have learned
about the natural world invites us to
accept uncertainty.

MICHAEL GUILLEN
b. 1950
American mathematician

The sea became my unspoken challenge; the wind, the tide, the fog, the ledge, the bell, the gull that cried help, the never-ending threat and bluff of weather.

E.B. WHITE
(1899–1985)
American writer

The river and everything I remembered about it became a possession to me, a personal, private possession, as nothing else in my life ever had. Now it ran nowhere but in my head, but there it ran as though immortality.... In me it still is, and will be until I die, green, rocky, deep, fast, slow, and beautiful beyond reality.

JAMES DICKEY
b. 1923
American writer

Forget not that the earth delights to feel
your bare feet and the winds long to play
with your hair.

KAHLIL GIBRAN
(1883–1931)
Syrian-American poet and painter

Sit outside at midnight and close your eyes; feel the grass, the air, the space. Listen to birds for ten minutes at dawn. Memorize a flower.

LINDA HASSELSTROM
20th-century American writer and rancher

...and under these high hills the river
Tilt gushing and winding over stones
and slates, and the hills and mountains
skirted at the bottom with beautiful trees;
the whole lit up by the sun; and the air
so pure and fine; but no description can
at all do it justice....

QUEEN VICTORIA
(1819–1901)
Queen of Great Britain

Among the scenes which are deeply impressed on my mind, none exceed in sublimity the primeval forests undefaced by the hand of man...no one can stand in these solitudes unmoved, and not feel that there is more in man than the mere breath of his body.

CHARLES DARWIN
(1809–1882)
English naturalist

My father considered a walk among
the mountains as the equivalent of
churchgoing.

ALDOUS HUXLEY
(1894–1963)
English writer

I believe in God, only I spell it Nature.

FRANK LLOYD WRIGHT
(1869–1959)
American architect

Nature is not only what is visible to the eye—it shows the inner images of the soul—the images on the back side of the eyes.

EDVARD MUNCH
(1863–1944)
Norwegian painter and printmaker

It is an outcome of faith that nature—as she is perceptible to our five senses—takes the character of such a well-formulated puzzle.

ALBERT EINSTEIN
(1879–1955)
German-born American physicist

...what I'm going to call nature is everything on this planet that is at least partially under the control of some other will than ours. Pure nature is of course what exists entirely without our will.

NOEL PERRIN
b. 1927
American writer

. . .watching something grow is good for morale. It helps you believe in life. . .

MYRON S. KAUFMANN
20th-century American writer

...everything that slows us down and forces patience, everything that sets us back into the slow cycles of nature, is a help. Gardening is an instrument of grace.

MAY SARTON
b. 1912
American writer

Except during the nine months before he draws his first breath, no man manages his affairs as well as a tree does.

GEORGE BERNARD SHAW
(1856–1950)
English playwright and writer

The Knowledge of Nature may be ornamental, and it may be useful; but if, to attain an Eminence in that, we neglect the Knowledge and Practice of essential Duties, we deserve Reprehension.

BENJAMIN FRANKLIN
(1706–1790)
American statesman, philosopher, and writer

Hurt not the earth, neither the sea, nor the trees.

THE BOOK OF REVELATION

Everything in nature invites us constantly to be what we are. We are often like rivers: careless and forceful, timid and dangerous, lucid and muddied, eddying, gleaming, still.

GRETEL EHRLICH
b. 1946
American writer

Even such a happy Child of earth am I;
Even as these blissful creatures do I fare;
Far from the world I walk, and from all care...

WILLIAM WORDSWORTH
(1770–1850)
English poet

*When the clouds rise in terraces of
white, soon will the country of the corn
priests be pierced with the arrows of rain.*

ZUÑI INDIAN SAYING

...in the night we wake and hear the rain,
Like mellow music, comforting the earth...

ROBERT BURNS WILSON
(1850–1916)
American painter and writer

Death falls, as at times it must, and Life springs in its place. Nature lives and journeys on and passes all about in well balanced, orderly array.

GREY OWL
(1888–1938)
British-born Canadian naturalist

Again rejoicing Nature sees
   Her robe assume its vernal
      hues
Her leafy locks wave in the
      breeze,
   All freshly steep'd in morning
      dews.

ROBERT BURNS
(1759–1796)
Scottish poet

The last fling of winter is over.....
The earth, the soil itself, has a dreaming
quality about it. It is warm now to the
touch; it has come alive; it hides secrets
that in a moment, in a little while, it
will tell.

DONALD CULROSS PEATTIE
(1898–1964)
American naturalist and writer

...the first day when everything is shining, and breaking up, when across the heavy streams, from the melting snow, there is already the scent of the thawing earth; when on the bare thawed places, under the slanting sunshine, the larks are singing confidingly, and, with glad splash and roar, the torrents roll from ravine to ravine.

IVAN TURGENEV
(1818–1883)
Russian writer

There was a kick, and a flop, and a popping, panting baby quail standing in the fierce sunshine. He caught his breath, took a squint at his hatcher in the sky and hiked for cover, still damp from the shell.

DALLAS LORE SHARP
(1870–1929)
American writer

Is not machinery linked with animal life
in an infinite variety of ways? The shell
of a hen's egg is made of a delicate white
ware and is a machine as much as an
egg-cup is...the hen makes the shell in
her inside, but it is pure pottery.

SAMUEL BUTLER
(1835–1902)
English writer

The sun, nurturing the green mountains and rivers, the boundless forest, the golden monkeys, and also our fellow human beings, seemed to me then the source of all energy and wisdom, and the greatest, most beautiful, immortal mother.

TANG XIYANG
b. 1930
Chinese naturalist and writer

The whole marvelous panorama of life that spreads over the surface of our globe is, in the last analysis, transformed sunlight.

ERNST HAECKEL
(1834–1919)
German biologist and philosopher

To me a lush carpet of pine needles or spongy grass is more welcome than the most luxurious Persian rug.

HELEN KELLER
(1880–1968)
American writer

The silence of snowy aisles of the forest, the whirring flight of partridges, the impudent bark of squirrels, the quavering voices of owls and coons, the music of the winds in the high trees—all these impressions unite in my mind like parts of a woodland symphony.

HAMLIN GARLAND
(1860–1940)
American writer

One evening, just as the sun was setting, a flock of large birds rose from the brushwood. The duckling had never seen anything so beautiful before; their plumage was of dazzling white, and they had long slender necks. They were swans. They uttered a singular cry, spread out their long, splendid wings, and flew away from these cold regions to warmer countries, across the sea.

HANS CHRISTIAN ANDERSEN
(1805–1875)
Danish writer

The migrating wild creatures...seem to link up animal life with the great currents of the globe. It is moving day on a continental scale. It is the call of the primal instinct to increase and multiply, suddenly setting in motion whole tribes and races.

JOHN BURROUGHS
(1837–1921)
American naturalist and writer

Each flower is a soul opening out to
nature.

GERARD DE NERVAL
(1808–1855)
French writer

E*very individual is an expression of the whole realm of nature, a unique action of the total universe.*

ALAN WATTS
b. 1915
English-born American philosopher

The loons of Lac la Croix are part of the vast solitudes, the hundreds of rocky islands, the long reaches of the lake.... My memory is full of their calling: in the morning when the white horses of the mists are galloping out of the bays, at midday when their long lazy bugling is part of the calm, and at dusk when their music joins with that of the hermit thrushes and the wilderness is going to sleep.

SIGURD F. OLSON
(1899–1982)
American writer and wildlife conservator

There through the northeast window, large and round and beautiful, shone the moon. . . . It was like the sudden meeting with a friend, reassuring, comforting. A broad band of light lay across my breast like a kind arm thrown over me. The path of the moonbeams on the water seemed the road to some safe haven. With the moon's calm face looking in and the soft lapping of the waves as lullaby, I fell asleep. . . .

LAURA LEE DAVIDSON
20th-century American educator and writer

We talk of our mastery of nature, which sounds very grand, but the fact is we respectfully adapt ourselves, first, to her ways.

CLARENCE DAY
(1874–1935)
American writer

Let us give Nature a chance; she knows
herself better than we do.

MICHEL E. DE MONTAIGNE
(1533–1592)
French essayist

One swallow does not make a summer,
but one skein of geese, cleaving the murk
of a March thaw, is the spring.

ALDO LEOPOLD
(1886–1948)
American writer and conservationist

The beautiful swallows, be tender to them, for they symbolize all that is best in nature and all that is best in our hearts.

RICHARD JEFFERIES
(1848–1887)
English naturalist and writer

T*he light air about me told me that the world ended here: only the ground and sun and sky were left, and if one went a little farther there would be only sun and sky, and one would float off into them, like the tawny hawks which sailed over our heads making slow shadows on the grass.*

WILLA CATHER
(1873–1947)
American writer

Morning-fair, follow me further back...
When the sun for me glinted the sides of a sand grain,
and my intent stretched over the buds at their first trembling.

THEODORE ROETHKE
(1908–1963)
American poet

Nature is no great mother who has borne us. She is our creation. It is in our brain that she quickens to life.

OSCAR WILDE
(1854–1900)
Irish poet and dramatist

It is the marriage of the soul with Nature that makes the intellect fruitful, and gives birth to imagination.

HENRY DAVID THOREAU
(1817–1862)
American essayist and poet

Owls are interesting birds to paint; with their round faces and forward looking eyes, they are the most human-looking of birds.

ROBERT BATEMAN
b. 1930
Canadian artist and naturalist

A re not the mountains, waves, and skies, a part
Of me and of my soul, as I of them?

LORD BYRON
(1788–1824)
English poet

Magic birds were dancing in the mystic marsh. The grass swayed with them, and the shallow waters, and the earth fluttered under them. The earth was dancing with the cranes, and the low sun, and the wind and sky.

MARJORIE KINNAN RAWLINGS
(1896–1953)
American writer

The one day recalls us to hills and meadows, to moss, roses, dirt, apples, and the breathing of timothy—away from the yellow chair, from blue smoke and daydream.

DONALD HALL
b. 1928
American poet

There is a moth so small that it can
walk through the eye of a needle and look
up at the arch overhead as at the ceiling
of an enormous gateway.

W.S. MERWIN
b. 1927
American writer and translator

How vast is creation! I see the planets rise and the stars hurry by, carried along with their light! What, then, is this hand which propels them?

GUSTAVE FLAUBERT
(1821–1880)
French writer

I*n nature there are neither rewards nor punishments—there are consequences.*

R.G. INGERSOLL
(1833–1899)
American attorney

M*en argue, nature acts.*

VOLTAIRE
(1694–1778)
French writer

Accuse not nature, she hath done her part;
Do thou but thine!

JOHN MILTON
(1608–1674)
English poet

The great illusion of the suburban experience was that man can experience nature by owning pieces of it. And that is fundamentally incorrect. Nature eludes ownership.

EDMUND N. BACON
b. 1910
American architect and city planner

You never conquer a mountain, you stand on the summit a few moments; then the wind blows your footprints away.

ARLENE BLUM
b. 1945
American biochemist and mountain climber

Remember what you have seen, because everything forgotten returns to the circling winds.

NAVAJO WIND CHANT

The first law of ecology is that
everything is related to everything else.

BARRY COMMONER
b. 1917
American microbiologist and writer

...a forest is changed
By a chameleon's tuning his skin to it...

RICHARD WILBUR
b. 1921
American poet

O*ne could not pluck a flower without troubling a star.*

LOREN EISELEY
(1907–1977)
American anthropologist

Flowers and even fruit are only the beginning. In the seed lies the life and the future.

MARION ZIMMER BRADLEY
b. 1930
American writer